THIS WALKER BOOK BELONGS TO:

_____

_____

_____

_____

First published 1989 by Walker Books Ltd
87 Vauxhall Walk, London SE11 5HJ

This edition published 1999

2 4 6 8 10 9 7 5 3

© 1989 Ron Maris

This book has been typeset in Garamond Educational.

Printed in Hong Kong

British Library Cataloguing in Publication Data
A catalogue record for this book is
available from the British Library.

ISBN 0-7445-6357-7

Runaway
Rabbit

Ron Maris

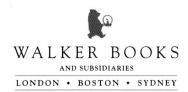

WALKER BOOKS
AND SUBSIDIARIES
LONDON • BOSTON • SYDNEY

Good morning,
Rabbit.

Into the house?

I don't think so!

Into the pipe?

Yes . . .

...and out again!

Hello, little duck.

Can I come in?

Run, Rabbit, run!

Where's Rabbit now?

There he is!

Here's a carrot
for you.

Got you!

Don't run away
again, Rabbit.